This Little Tiger book belongs to:

_____

_____

_____

For my friend, Liz ~ C F

To my two little angels, Abigail and William
— you're my inspiration ~ G Y

LITTLE TIGER PRESS
An imprint of Magi Publications
1 The Coda Centre, 189 Munster Road, London SW6 6AW
www.littletigerpress.com

First published in Great Britain 2008
This edition published 2008

Text copyright © Claire Freedman 2008
Illustrations copyright © Gail Yerrill 2008
Claire Freedman and Gail Yerrill have asserted their rights to be identified as the author
and illustrator of this work under the Copyright, Designs and Patents Act, 1988

A CIP catalogue record for this book is available from the British Library

Printed in China
2 4 6 8 10 9 7 5 3 1

The Christmas Angels

CLAIRE FREEDMAN

Illustrated by GAIL YERRILL

LITTLE TIGER PRESS
London

Hush now, can you hear
the angels singing,
High up in the
frosty midnight air?
Voices ringing, singing
songs of Christmas,
Happiness for all
the world to share.

As we count the days
until it's Christmas,
Filling all our homes
with light and love,
Angels share these
special times of gladness,
Celebrating with us
high above.

As the snowflakes float like stars from heaven,

Angels touch them softly, one by one,

Giving each a gentle angel blessing,

Snowflakes sent with love for everyone.

When we gather round
to sing sweet carols,
Each of us with
happy heart aglow,
In the sky, the angels
all sing with us,
As on that first
Christmas long ago.

By our sides, our caring

guardian angels

Look out for us,

each and every day.

So, however far from

home we travel,

Loving angels help

us on our way.

When we help and care

for one another,

High above, the angels

see it too.

Every little act of

love and kindness,

Makes the gentle angels

smile at you.

As dusk falls, the angels fly above us,

Lighting all the stars up in the sky.

When you see a silver star shine brightly,

Then you know an angel is nearby.

Angels sing their songs
of treasured friendship,

Special moments,

sharing everything,

Songs about our

happy times together,

And the warmth that

loving friendships bring.

As the daylight fades
to gentle shadows,
And soft moonbeams
shimmer, silver-white,
Tender angels watch us
while we're sleeping,
Keeping us safe through
the moonlit night.

Hush now, can you hear the angels singing?

Sweetest songs of peace from heaven above,

Christmas songs of hope and joy and wonder,

Filling every happy heart with love.

Your little angels will love these titles from Little Tiger Press

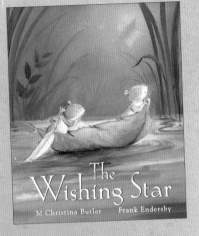

The Wishing Star
M Christina Butler · Frank Endersby

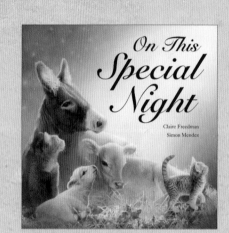

On This Special Night
Claire Freedman
Simon Mendez

The Magic of Christmas
Claire Freedman
Gail Yerrill

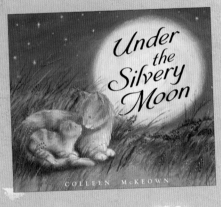

Under the Silvery Moon
COLLEEN McKEOWN

One Magical Christmas
Alice Wood

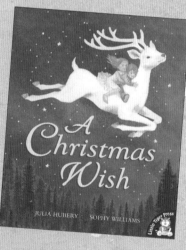

A Christmas Wish
JULIA HUBERY · SOPHY WILLIAMS

For information regarding any of the above titles
or for our catalogue, please contact us:
Little Tiger Press, 1 The Coda Centre,
189 Munster Road, London SW6 6AW
Tel: 020 7385 6333 Fax: 020 7385 7333
E-mail: info@littletiger.co.uk www.littletigerpress.com